Look at Me I'm going to Spain!

This book is dedicated
to my daughter
Carmela

First published in 2022 by Daniel Williamson
www.danielwilliamson.co.uk
This edition published in 2022
Text © Daniel Williamson 2022
Illustrations © Kleverton Monteiro 2022
Cover design © by Uzuri Designs 2022

ISBN: 978-1-913583-25-5

DW

www.danielwilliamson.co.uk

Look at Me
I'm going to
Spain!

I woke up so excited today, because today I'm going to Spain for the first time ever! I just can't wait!

¡Hoy me he despertado muy emocionado porque viajo a España por primera vez! ¡Me muero de ganas!

At the airport I got to have my photo taken
with the pilot before our flight to Madrid.

En el aeropuerto, me hice una foto con
el piloto antes de despegar hacia Madrid.

When we arrived in Madrid I met my Spanish family. They were very happy to see me. They brought their puppy to meet me, his name is Milú.

Al llegar a Madrid, conocí a mi familia española. Estaban muy felices de verme. Trajeron a su perro para que me conociera. Se llama Milú.

We went to the family home and had a traditional Spanish meal. We ate croquettes, paella and Spanish omelette. I love Spanish food!

Fuimos a casa de la familia y probamos platos tradicionales. Comimos croquetas, paella y tortilla de patata. ¡Me encanta la comida española!

After dinner my uncle played a famous Spanish song on his Spanish guitar. The song was called "Between two waters". Spanish music is beautiful!

Después de cenar, mi tío tocó una canción típica con la guitarra española. La canción se titulaba «Entre dos aguas». ¡La música española es muy bonita!

At bedtime my grandmother read me a story called *Garbancito*. It's about a little boy as small as a chickpea, a bit naughty, but very smart.

A la hora de dormir, mi abuela me leyó el cuento *Garbancito*. Va sobre un niño tan pequeño como un garbanzo, un poco travieso, pero muy listo.

The next day we went to see the royal palace.
This building is enormous and is the official residence
of the king but he doesn't live there.

Al día siguiente, fuimos a ver el Palacio Real.
Este edificio es enorme y es la residencia
oficial del rey, pero no vive allí.

Then we went to a museum called "Museo Arqueológico Nacional". I saw mosaics, historical sculptures and objects from Roman times.'

Luego fuimos al Museo Arqueológico Nacional. Vi mosaicos, esculturas históricas y objetos de la época romana.

We then went to another museum called "Museo del Prado" and I saw some art by a famous Spanish man called Velazquez. His paintings are amazing, I wish I could paint like that!

Después fuimos al Museo del Prado y vi algunas pinturas de Velázquez, un famosísimo pintor español. Sus cuadros son increíbles. ¡Ojalá yo pintara tan bien!

Outside the museum was a man selling 'churros'.
It's a very typical and tasty Spanish snack.
I ate two of them all by myself.

Fuera del museo, un hombre vendía churros.
Es un merienda muy típica y está riquísimo.
Me comí dos churros.

We walked to the town square and saw two people dancing flamenco. It's a beautiful dance.
It was wonderful to watch.

Fuimos andando hacia el centro de la ciudad y vimos dos personas bailando flamenco. Es un baile precioso.
Me encantó verlo.

In the afternoon we went to the Santiago Bernabeu stadium to watch the Spanish team play football. A nice lady gave me a Spanish flag to wave!

Por la tarde fuimos al estadio Santiago Bernabéu para ver a la selección española jugar al fútbol. ¡Una amable señora me dio una bandera de España para que la ondeara!

Football was really fun! Dad bought me a T-Shirt like the players. I was shouting "go on Spain!" and "one more goal!"

¡Lo pasamos muy bien! Mi padre me regaló una camiseta como la de los jugadores. Grité: «ánimo España» y «un gol más».

After the match we went to a restaurant for more yummy Spanish food. I had 'callos madrileños' and Spanish almond cake for dessert.

Después del partido, fuimos a un restaurante para cenar más comida típica riquísima. Me comí unos callos madrileños y tarta de Santiago de postre.

The waiter was really funny. He even did a magic trick just for me. His name was Pablo and he is from Sevilla.

El camarero fue muy gracioso. Incluso hizo un truco de magia solo para mí. Se llamaba Pablo y era de Sevilla.

In the morning it was really sunny and we all went to an orchard. Figs grow a lot here. I picked some from the trees.

Por la mañana, hacía mucho sol y visitamos un huerto. En esta zona hay muchos higos. Recolecté algunos de los árboles.

I met a nice lady there and she was wearing
a 'chulapa' dress. It's a traditional dress in Madrid
for San Isidro and La Paloma saint's day .

Conocí una guapa mujer que llevaba un vestido
de chulapa. Es un traje típico de Madrid
en las fiestas de San Isidro y de la Paloma.

In the car I heard different Spanish music called "La Macarena". I liked this Spanish music too, it made me want to dance!

En el coche escuché una canción española que se titula *La Macarena*. Este tipo de música también me gustó mucho, ¡me dieron ganas de bailar!

We drove past an old famous monument
called la Puerta de Alcalá. It's famous because
it used to be one of the five historical city gates
that gave access to the city.
Desde el coche, vimos un monumento muy conocido:
la Puerta de Alcalá. Es famoso porque era una de las
cinco puertas reales que daban acceso a la ciudad.

Back at the house, on our last night, the family all played a game together called 'parchis' with Spanish cards. It was really fun!

Durante la última noche, cuando volvimos a casa, jugué con toda la familia al parchís ¡Fue muy divertido!

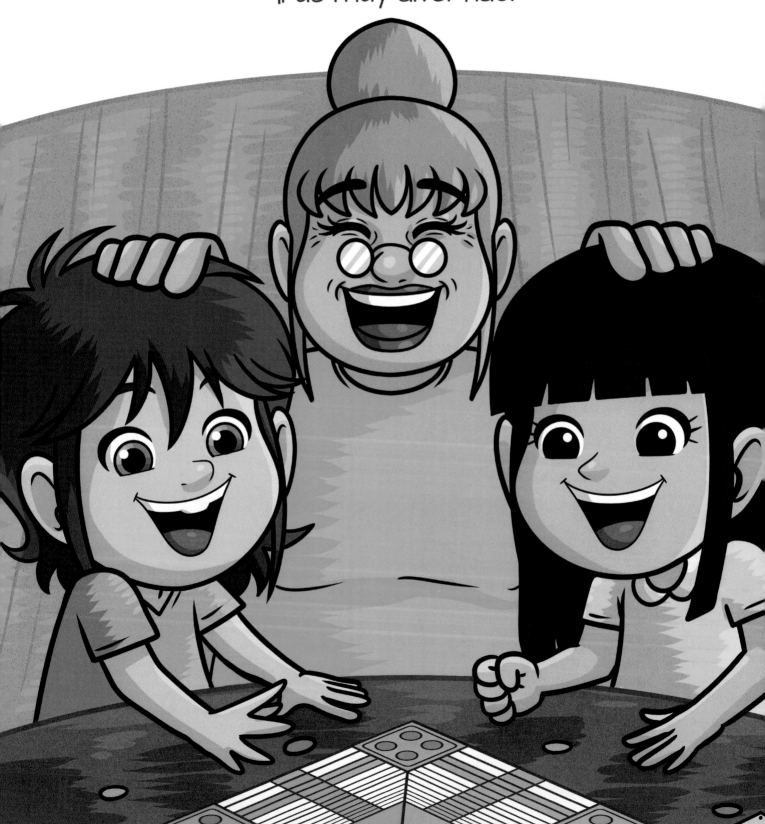

Before I went to bed my Spanish family gave me a present each to remind me of Spain. They gave me a Spanish fan, some castanets and some serrano ham.

Antes de irme a la cama, cada miembro de mi familia española me dio un regalo para acordarme de España. Me regalaron un abanico, unas castañuelas y jamón serrano.

I really love it in Spain! The only problem is I can't decide what's my favourite thing.

¡Me encanta España! El único problema es que no puedo decidir qué es lo que más me gusta.

Was it the yummy Spanish food, the wonderful Spanish music, watching Spain play football, or the beautiful Spanish dancing?......

¿Fue la riquísima comida española, la maravillosa música, ver jugar a la selección o el precioso baile?

Or was it the artwork by Velazquez, the beautiful Spanish buildings, the interesting Spanish stories, or spending time with my amazing Spanish family?...

¿O fueron los cuadros de Velázquez, los bonitos edificios, las interesantes historias o pasar el tiempo con mi increíble familia española?

I just can't decide because I love everything here!
So much so, in fact...

¡Creo que no puedo decidirme porque me encanta
todo! De hecho, me gusta tanto que...

I've already asked to come back real soon.
Again and again and again!

Ya he pedido volver muy pronto. ¡Una y mil veces!

This author has developed a bilingual book series designed to introduce children to a number of new languages from a very young age.

If you enjoyed reading this story, you will undoubtedly like popular rhyming picture books from this author which are also currently available.

A Message From The Author

I'd like to say a massive thank you to every single child and adult that read one of my books! My dream is to bring cultures together through fun illustrations, imagination and creativity via the power of books.

If you would like to join me on this journey, please visit my website danielwilliamson.co.uk where each email subscriber receives a free ebook to keep or we will happily send to a friend of your choice as a gift!

Nothing makes me happier than a review on the platform you purchased my book telling me where my readers are from! Also, please click on my links below and follow me to join my ever-growing online family! Remember there is no time like the present and the present is a gift!

Yours gratefully

Daniel Williamson

@DanWAuthor

@danwauthor

@DanWAuthor

Made in the USA
Las Vegas, NV
19 January 2024

84601180R00021